Reading STREET
Grade 2

Scott Foresman

Strategic Intervention Decodable Readers

PEARSON
Scott
Foresman

Editorial Offices: Glenview, Illinois • Parsippany, New Jersey • New York, New York
Sales Offices: Needham, Massachusetts • Duluth, Georgia • Glenview, Illinois
Coppell, Texas • Sacramento, California • Mesa, Arizona

ISBN: 0-328-14508-4

6 7 8 9 10 V084 14 13 12 11 10 09 08 07

Contents

Strategic Intervention Decodable Reader 5

Shane

Written by Renée McLean

Illustrated by Sam Mok

Phonics Skill

Consonant Digraphs ch, tch, sh, th, wh

Shane	chased	bush	when	itch	scratched
chin	shin	chest	that	itching

Mom said, "Shane, some plants can make you itch. You should not go back there."

8

Shane chased his pup Spot.
Spot had gone through a bush.
When Shane came out,
he had an itch.

2

His mom put some
wet and pink stuff on his itch.
That itching stopped at last.

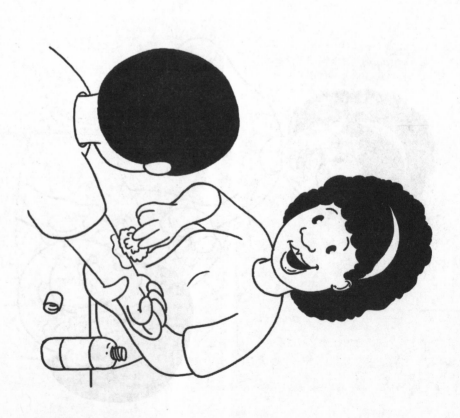

7

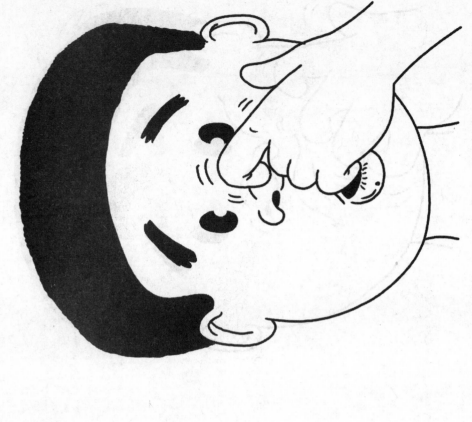

Shane had an itch
on his nose.
Shane scratched it.

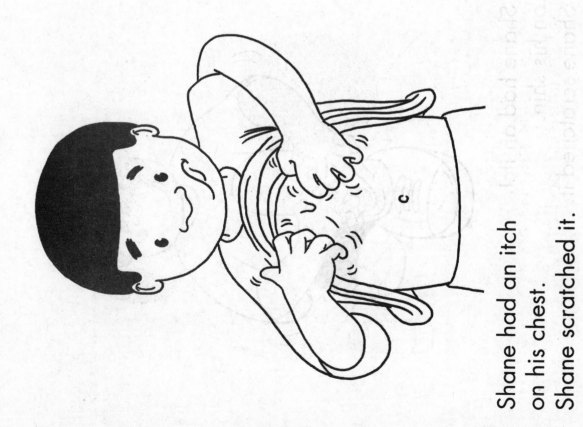

Shane had an itch
on his chest.
Shane scratched it.

Shane had an itch
on his chin.
Shane scratched it.

4

Shane had an itch
on his shin.
Shane scratched it.

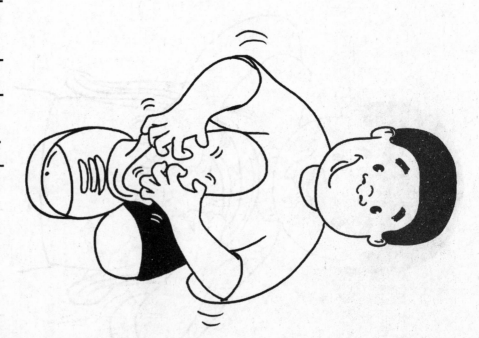

5

A Gift for the Family

Written by Marcie Watson
Illustrated by Kelly Parmont

Phonics Skills

R-controlled ar, or		Syllables VCCV	
hard	for	baskets	ribbon
car	yard	darling	kitten
horse	porch		
jars	darling		

Brett petted his kitten.
Brett is glad that
Dad got this gift.

8

It is hard sitting still.
Dad was getting
a gift for his family.
"I will listen for Dad's car,"
Brett said.

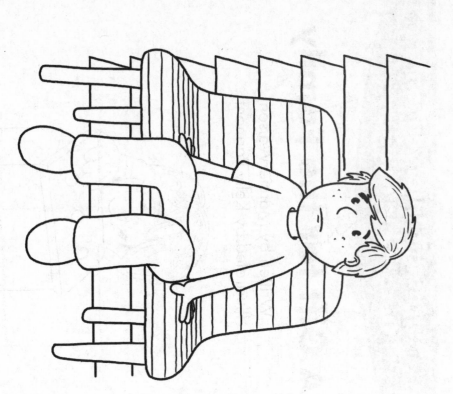

2

Brett pulled off the ribbon.
Brett lifted the lid.
It is a darling kitten!

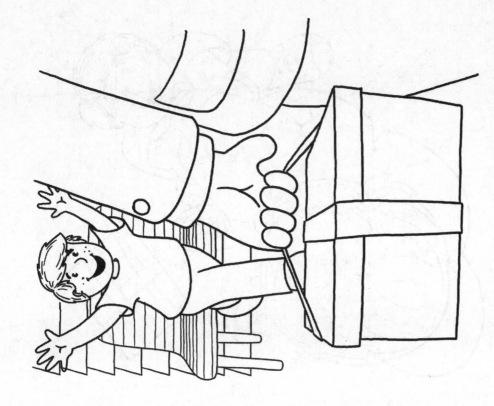

Brett heard Dad's car
while sitting in his yard.
Brett rushed in at once.
What gift had Dad gotten?

Dad pulled that box close.
"Time for this gift!" Dad said
with a quick wink.

4

"Can I see it?"
Brett begged.
"What can it be?"
Dad asked.

Is it a rocking horse?
Is it a porch swing?
Is it jars of jam?
Is it plants in baskets?

JAM
JAM

5

Stuck

Written by Dan Archer

Illustrated by Jolie Foster

Phonics Skill

Contractions n't, 's, 'll

| it's | let's | that's | can't | I'll | hadn't | wasn't |

Liz and Brad laughed as they went back home. "You're still great, Dad," his kids added.

8

Liz and Brad looked up.
"A cat is sitting on that second branch,"
Brad said.
"It's stuck," Liz added.

2

Dad did his best.
Dad stretched up.
That cat jumped off!
That cat wasn't stuck!

7

"Let's run and tell Dad," Brad said.
Those kids ran five blocks.
Dad was sitting on his porch.

"Can you get it?" Brad asked.
"I certainly can," Dad bragged.
"I'll either stretch up
or stand on that crate."

"There is a cat that's stuck," Liz said.
"It can't jump off the branch."
"Will you help?" Brad asked.

"I'll help," Dad said.
Dad, Liz, and Brad went back
to that sad cat.
It hadn't left the branch.

Strategic Intervention
Decodable Reader 8

Curt's Bike Trouble

Written by Amanda Hopkins
Illustrated by Christopher Calvetti

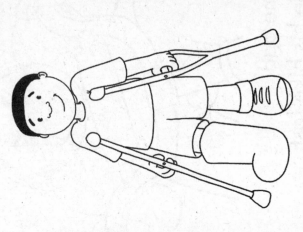

Phonics Skills

R-controlled er, ir, ur			Syllable -er
Curt	turned	swerve	dirt	curb	corner
Curt's	hurt	Fern	Nurse	Kirk	plaster
hurting	perked	first			better

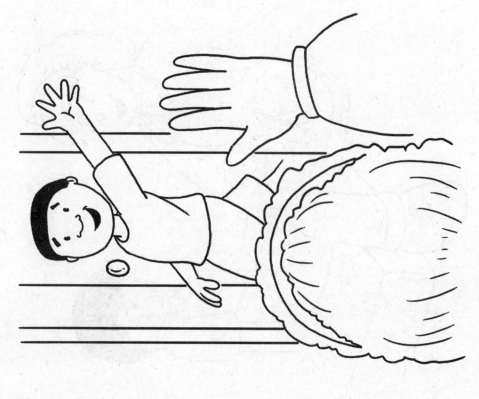

"I will ride well,"
Curt said.
"I had that big cast on
for long enough!"

8

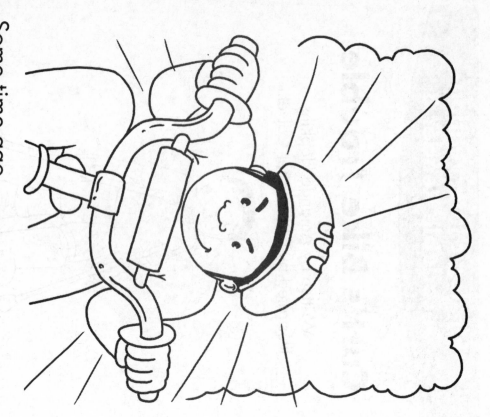

Some time ago,
Curt rode his bike fast.
He turned at this corner
and rode toward a big hole.

2

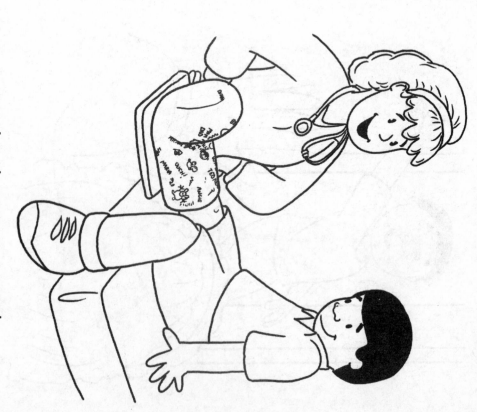

Curt went back to Nurse Kirk.
"This leg is better," Nurse Kirk said.
"You must look first
and not ride fast."

7

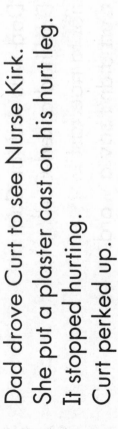

Curt did not swerve.
His bike hit that big hole.
Curt fell hard in the dirt
by the curb.

Dad drove Curt to see Nurse Kirk.
She put a plaster cast on his hurt leg.
It stopped hurting.
Curt perked up.

Curt's leg hurt.
Fern helped him.
She yelled for Curt's dad.

4

Dad was sad for Curt.
Dad had asked Curt
not to ride fast.
Curt didn't say a word.

5

Strategic Intervention Decodable Reader 9

Stan

Written by Joshua Blake

Illustrated by Ben Starkman

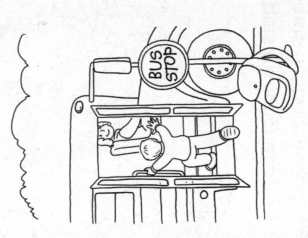

Phonics Skill

Plurals -s, -es

	notes	cards	dishes
	lamps	things	
lunches			
switches			

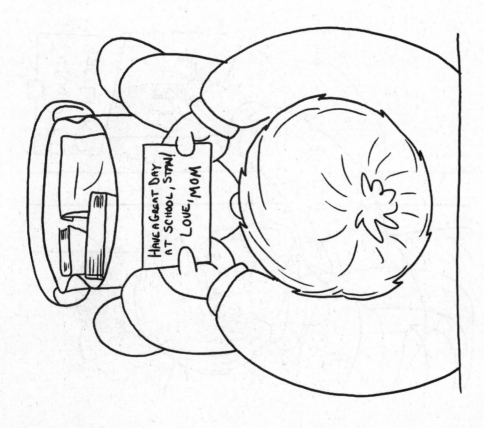

This is a big day for Stan!
Stan did not forget things—
thanks to Mom's notes.

Stan forgets his lunches.
Stan forgets his bag.
Stan can probably forget his name!

This note by Stan's door
tells him to flip these switches.
Stan turns off lamps.

It isn't pleasant to forget.
"People remember better with notes,"
Stan's mom said.
She bought cards
and made notes for Stan.

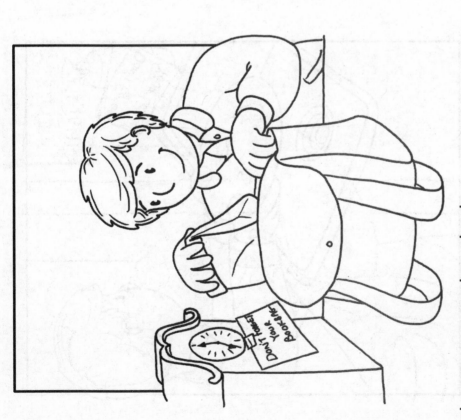

This note on the clock
tells Stan to grab
his big bag.
Stan slips it on his back.

4

This note on his cup
tells Stan to put dishes away.
Stan takes them to the sink.

This note at the sink
tells Stan to grab lunch.
Stan stuffs his lunch
in his bag.

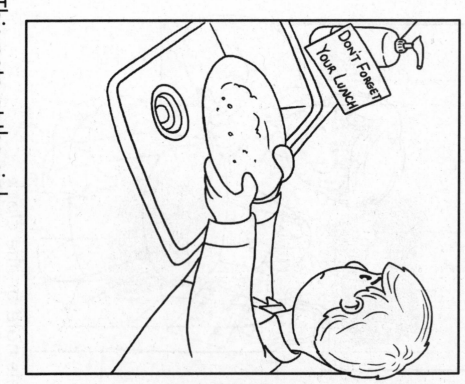

5

Jumping Jack

Written by Jessica Twining
Illustrated by Nicolas Florino

Phonics Skills

Long a: ai, ay		Syllables VCV
	playing	began
	way	ever
wait	plays	
say	day	
rained	play	
	may	

Kim smiled.
"That's fine," Kim said.
"Let's play that game."

8

Jack likes to hide and wait.
Jack likes to jump up fast.

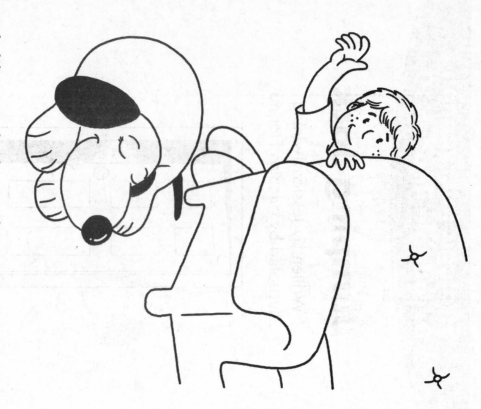

2

"I'm sorry for jumping out, Kim,"
Jack said.
"I promise not to do it ever again."

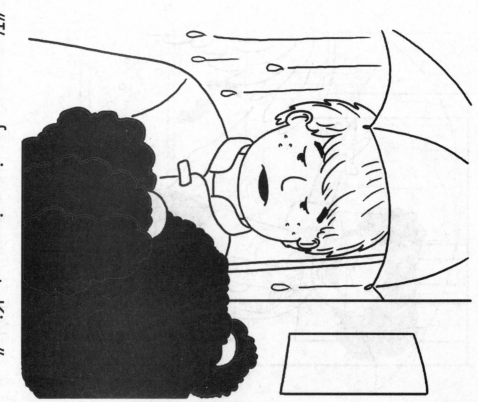

7

Jack thinks it is fun
playing this way.
Mom and Dad say that it is not nice.
Jack will not make friends
if he plays that way.

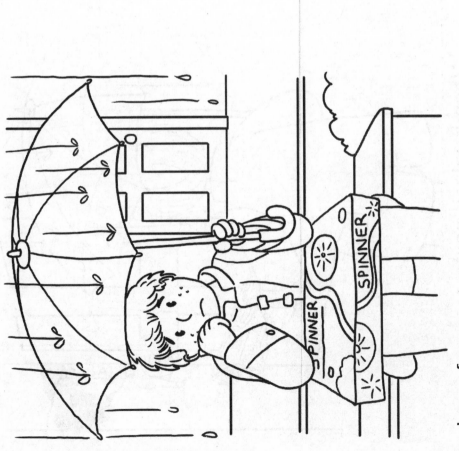

Jack sat for a minute.
"It is not the best plan
to jump out," Jack said.
"It may make people mad at me."

One day Jack hid behind his door.
When Kim came,
Jack jumped out at her.
Kim got mad and began yelling.
Then Kim went back home.

4

When it rained next,
Jack brought his best game
and asked Kim to play it with him.
Kim would not play.
Jack felt bad.

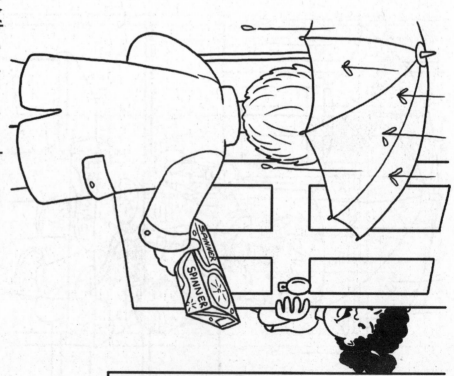

5

**Strategic Intervention
Decodable Reader 11**

What Did We Do Today?

Written by Karen Junias
Illustrated by Jeff Marshall

Phonics Skills

Long e: e, ee, ea, y				Syllables VCV
we	three	easy	green	tree	teacher
leaping	leaves	funny	beans	beets	city
windy	Jean	Bree	team	Jean's	robins
very	Bree's	silly	each	teacher	
read(s)	story	he	leave	week	
city					

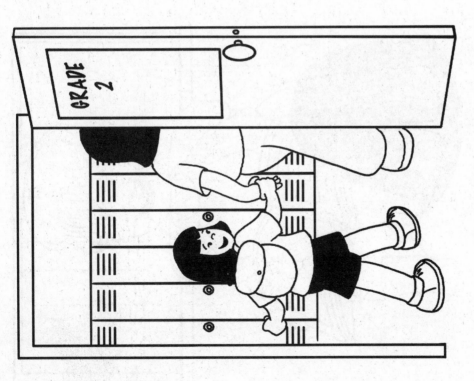

I guess we must leave for now.
Next week we will read about a city
and watch red robins.
I can't wait!

In math we added.
What is three plus three?
That is easy!
Three plus three is six.

2

Each day, the teacher reads us a tale.
This is a story about an elf.
He came to a village
and helped a man make shoes.

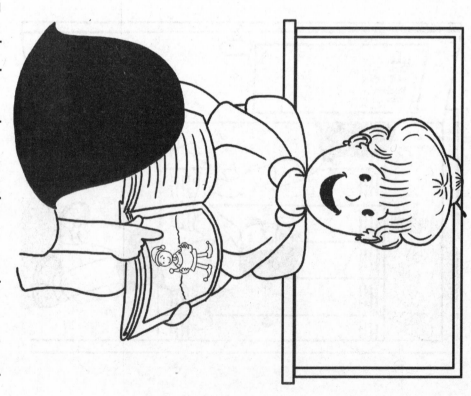

7

In science we watched
green tree frogs
leaping on leaves.
Those frogs are funny.

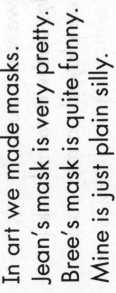

In art we made masks.
Jean's mask is very pretty.
Bree's mask is quite funny.
Mine is just plain silly.

At lunch we had
green beans or red beets.
I chose green beans because
I like them better.

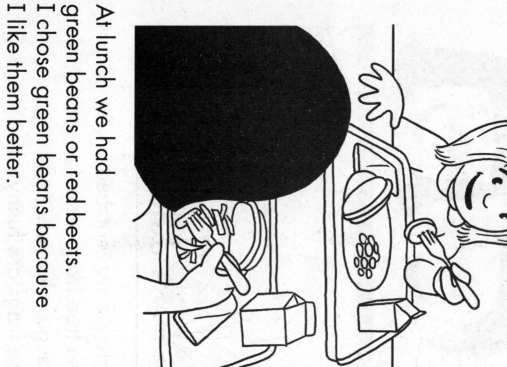

4

After lunch we went out.
It was windy, and we went back in.
Jean and Bree played on my team.
We won!

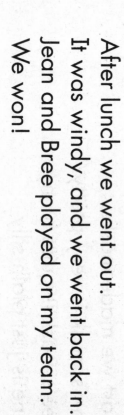

5

**Strategic Intervention
Decodable Reader 12**

A Day Off from School

Written by Michael Carlson
Illustrated by Ronda Miller

Phonics Skills

Long o: o, oa, ow, and oCC pattern (-ost, -old)			Syllables VCV
Joan	told	Joan's	old	teacher
goat	yellow	hold	showed	opened
bowl	most	scolded	toast	
glowed	opened	slow	go	

"That's the last stop!" Mom said.
"Let's go home
and eat dinner."

Joan asked,
"Is it time?"
"Hop in the car,"
Dad told Joan.

They opened the door
and left for home.
It had been a long day!
Joan's tired feet went slow.

Joan's parents drove her to a farm.
Joan petted fat pink pigs
and an old gray goat.
She saw cute yellow chicks.
"May I hold them?" she asked.

Joan's parents drove to her school.
Her teacher told them that Joan
always has good answers in math.
Joan's face glowed with pride.

Farmer Jed showed Joan
how to brush the horse.
"Grab a cube from the green bowl,"
Jed told Joan.
"Those are what she likes most."

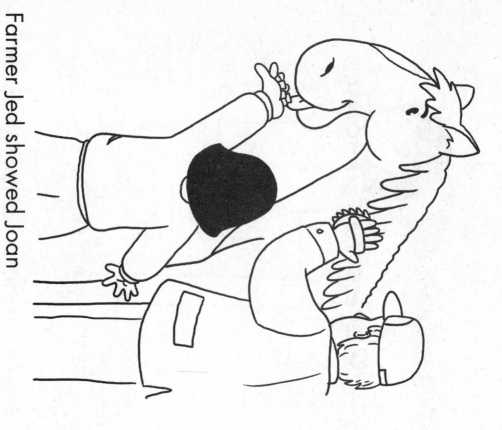

4

Mom, Dad, and Joan
drove to an old shop for lunch.
"First wash those hands,"
Mom scolded.
Then Joan had ham and toast.

5

Strategic Intervention
Decodable Reader 13

Parks and Picnics

Written by Eric Vincent

Illustrated by Samantha Roberts

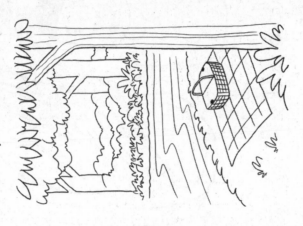

Phonics Skill

Compound Words

weekend	granddad	someone	riverbank	catfish
cannot	baseball	birthday	lunchtime	backyard
whatever	mailbox	grandparents	driveway	everyone

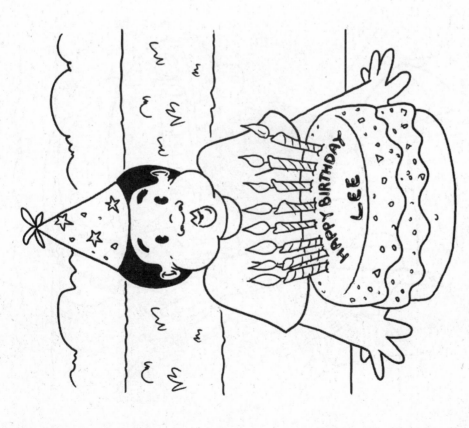

Then Lee had lunch
with everyone in his backyard.
It was a fun party.

8

Lee went to a park
this weekend.
He rode with his mom
and granddad.

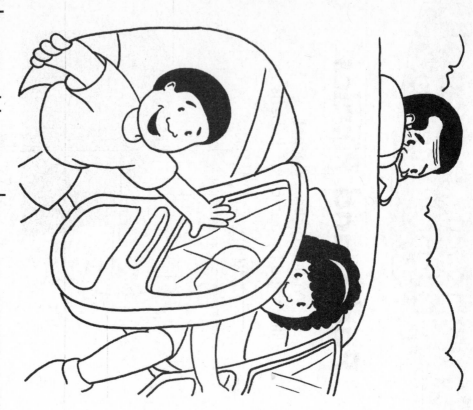

2

Today Lee saw birthday
cards in his mailbox.
His grandparents drove up
in the driveway.

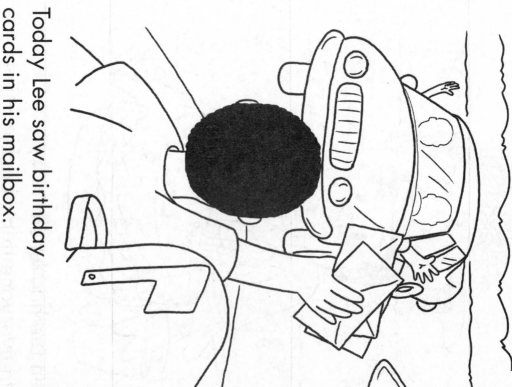

7

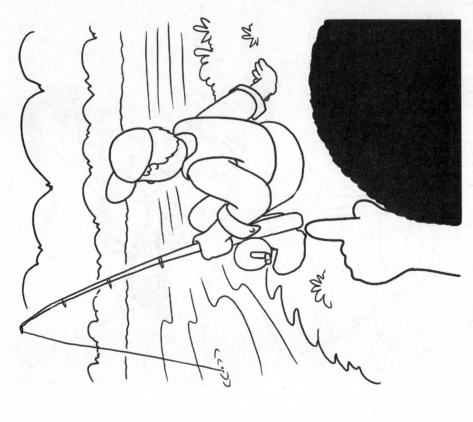

That park was big and nice.
Lee saw someone fishing
on the riverbank.
"Let's go!" he yelled.

"Tomorrow is my birthday,"
Lee told his granddad at lunchtime.
"We are having a backyard picnic.
We will eat whatever Dad makes."

Lee and his granddad went fishing.
Lee had never been fishing before.
Finally, he caught an ugly catfish.
"I cannot believe how big
this fish is!" Lee yelled.

4

Three kids asked Lee
to play baseball with them.
His mom made yummy snacks
while she waited for him.

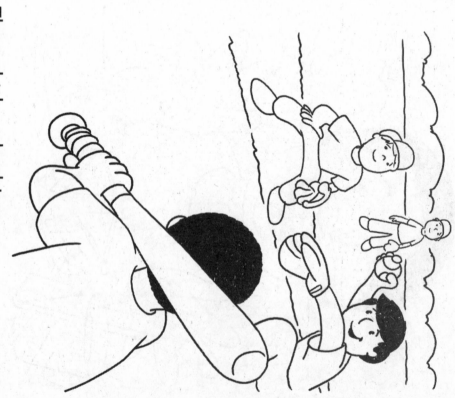

5

About Kay

Written by Daniele Wood
Illustrated by Lisa Mendoza

Phonics Skills

Long i: i, igh, y				Syllables VCV
bright	child	kind	finds	spider
spider	tiny	I	by	tiny
myself	mind	right	right	before
sky	nightlight			

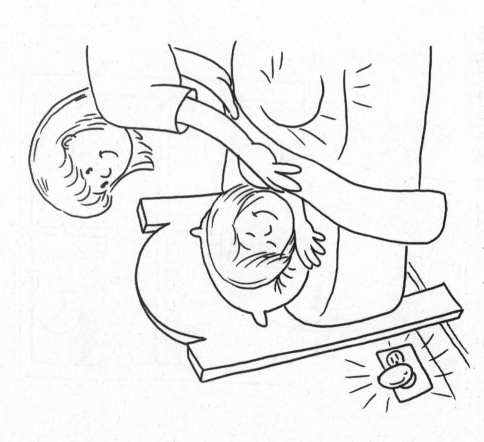

Kay sees it is bedtime.
She sleeps alone.
Her mom tucks her in
and leaves her nightlight on.

8

Kay is one
of three daughters.
Kay's age is half the age
of her big sister.
Kay is a bright child.

2

In the night sky,
Kay sees many stars.
She makes a wish on
one bright star.

7

Kay is kind.
She finds a spider
and tells her sister,
"It's a tiny spider.
Don't scare it."

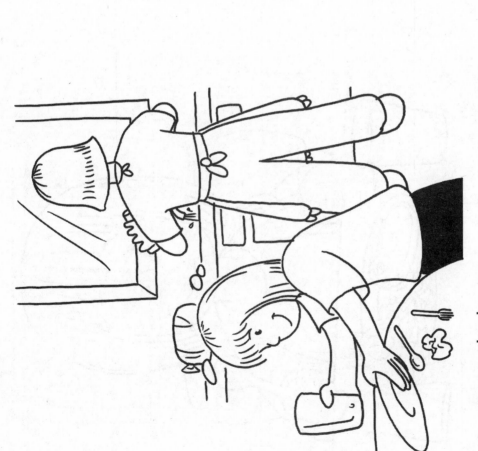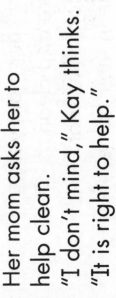

Her mom asks her to
help clean.
"I don't mind," Kay thinks.
"It is right to help."

Kay likes to play
with her sisters.
"But sometimes I like to play
by myself," she adds.

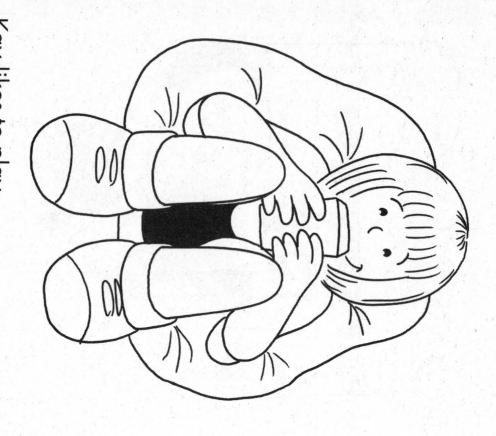

4

"Dinnertime!" her mom yells.
Kay gets nice and clean
before she takes her seat.
That is a rule in their home.

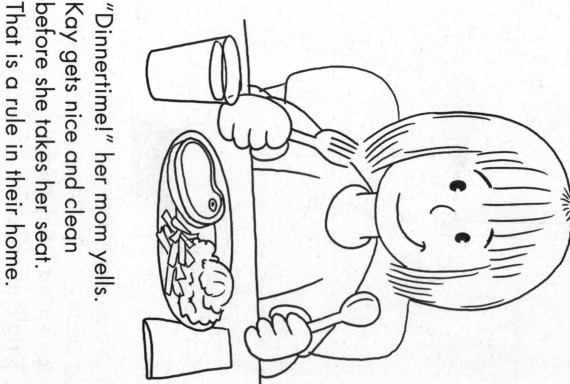

5

Jake's Shopping Trip

Written by Julia Liu

Illustrated by Bernie Zimmer

Phonics Skill

Comparative Endings -er, -est

bigger	closest	biggest	nicer	longer
brighter	thinnest	thicker	happier	highest
finest	nicest	happiest		

Jake had only one question.

"Can we get snacks?" he asked.

Mom got them hot popcorn.

It was the nicest, happiest part
of Jake's day.

8

2

"My clothes don't fit!" Jake cried.
"You are bigger," Mom said.
"We will go shopping."

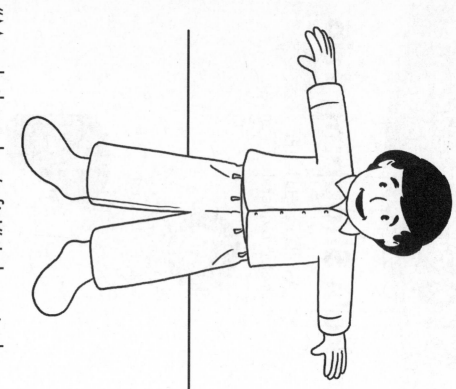

They shopped for shoes last.
"Those shoes on the highest shelf are the finest," the clerk noted.
"We'll take them," Mom said.
She gave that clerk money.

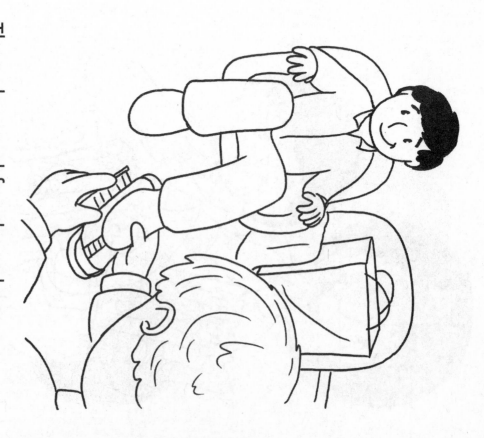

7

Mom parked in the closest spot
at the biggest store.
"This store closes in three hours,"
she noted.

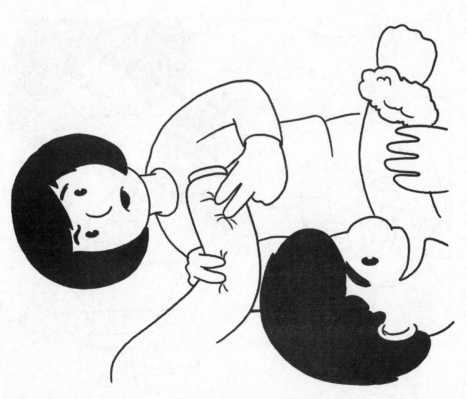

Then they shopped for a coat.
"This is the thinnest cloth," Mom said.
"That thicker coat makes
me happier."

Mom and Jake shopped for pants.
"These pants are nicer," Jake said.
"But those pants are longer,"
Mom added.

Next they shopped for shirts.
"Try that brighter shirt," Mom said.
"I like longer sleeves," Jake said.

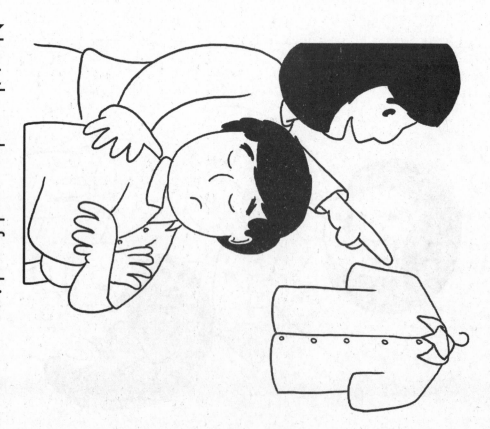

Strategic Intervention
Decodable Reader 16

Finding the Maple Tree

Written by Kara Linden

Illustrated by Paul Kim

Phonics Skill

Syllables Consonant + le

maple	simple	stumble	table	bottle
bubbles	able	puddle	giggle	

This is it!

This is the big maple tree for you to see.

We can sit under this tree.

We can giggle under this tree.

Why did you want to find this tree?

8

Have you seen that old maple tree?
It's simple to find the maple tree.
Stan can show the way!
He can run fast.
Can you?

2

Off we go!
Jump over that big puddle
but don't step in.
Keep running.
The hardest part is over.

7

Run by this big rock.
Do not stumble!
Turn right when you
pass this rock.

Kids are blowing bubbles!
We will blow bubbles too.
Stan is able to blow big bubbles.

Kids are playing hopscotch.
It's not a hard game to play.
Run by that game.
Sit at that table.

4

It's time to rest!
We'll find the maple tree,
but first we'll drink the water
in this bottle.

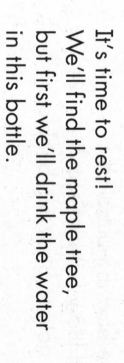

5

Strategic Intervention
Decodable Reader 17

Kevin Hooks a Fish

Written by Natalie Lohrman

Illustrated by Jim Petro

Phonics Skill

Vowels oo, u as in book, put

| brook | full | shook | stood | look |
| hooks | put | hook | pulled | hooked |

Kevin hooked a big lake fish!
When will Max hook a big lake fish?

2

Max and Kevin felt bored.
"Let's fish at the brook," said Kevin.
"No, let's fish at the lake," said Max.
"It is full of fish."

Then there was a splash and a tug.
"I have a fish on my hook!"
yelled Kevin.
Kevin pulled hard on his line.

7

"Are the fishing poles
in this box?" asked Max.
Kevin shook the big box.
His poles fell out.
"Let's go," he said.

Kevin and Max stood for
a long time waiting for fish.
"When will those fish bite?" asked Max.

"Look!" yelled Kevin.
"The lake is close!
Let's race to that tree."
Kevin and Max ran to the tree
that stood by the lake.

4

Kevin and Max checked
their fishing hooks.
"Let's put our lines in," said Max.
They dropped the fishing lines in.

5

Strategic Intervention
Decodable Reader 18

A Downtown Day

Written by Janis Jay
Illustrated by Jenna Clark

Phonics Skill

Vowel Diphthongs ou, ow /ou/

our	house	downtown	mouth	frown
loud	sounds	growls	gown	crowd
down	clown	bounced	around	how
towers	ground	flowers	now	

Mandy is tired now.
She cannot hear
the bus's loud sounds
on the way home.

8

"Let's not stay at our house," said Mom.
"Let's go downtown." Mandy grinned.
Her mouth cannot frown
if she is going downtown!

2

"Look at those flowers!" said Mandy.
Mandy stopped and smelled
a bunch of roses.

7

They took a bus.
"This bus makes loud sounds!"
yelled Mandy over the growls
and rumbles of that bus.

Downtown has towers
that stretch to the sky.
Mandy looks up to the top.
Mandy cannot look down at the ground
when she visits downtown!

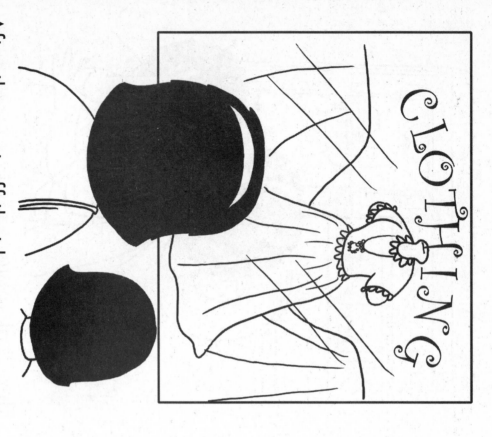

After they got off that bus,
Mandy and her mom shopped.
"Look at that nice gown," said Mom.
"It could be for a queen!"

They saw a crowd down the street.
The crowd was by a funny clown.
He bounced around.
"How did he do that?" Mandy asked.

Strategic Intervention Decodable Reader 19

Joy Asks Why

Written by Daniel Suh
Illustrated by Nick Thivel

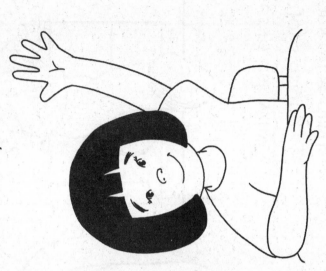

Phonics Skill

Vowel Diphthongs oi, oy /oi/

| Joy | enjoys | soil | moist |
| noise | voices | cowboy | enjoy |

"Joy, why do you enjoy
asking questions so much?"
Joy's classmates asked.
"I just like to be told why!"
answered Joy.

8

Joy likes to ask why.
She enjoys asking
questions each day!
Joy thinks of questions
on her way to school.

2

"Miss Smith, why is the man
in this book sitting on a horse?"
Joy asked.
"Joy, that man is a cowboy,"
answered the teacher.

7

"Tim, why is this soil wet?"
Joy asked.
"It rained last night, Joy,"
Tim answered.

"Jen, why do we use
our voices in this class?"
Joy asked.
"Joy, we use voices to sing songs,"
Jen answered.

"Pam, why is your shirt moist?"
Joy asked.
"I spilled water on it,"
Pam answered.

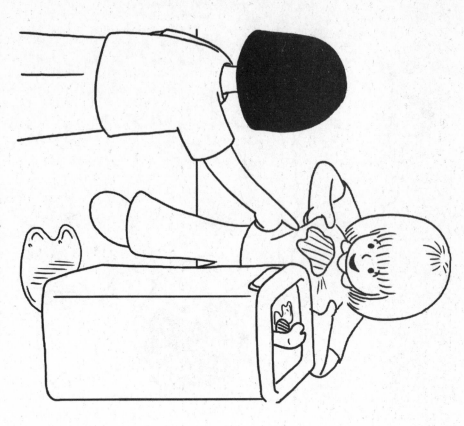

"Nate, why is that bell
making noise?" Joy asked.
"It's ringing to tell us
that class will start,"
Nate answered.

Tick, Tock

Written by Laura Nguyen
Illustrated by Tony Flint

Phonics Skill

Vowel Patterns oo, ue, ew, ui as in moon

| clue | blue | room | broom | new | noon |
| food | cool | juice | tooth | bathroom | clues |

The timer went "ding!"
No new clues can be found.
Mom, show me where
the timer is now!

8

I hear it go tick. I hear it go tock.
Mom gave me a clue
to find her blue timer.
It said, "Go to the room
with the big broom."

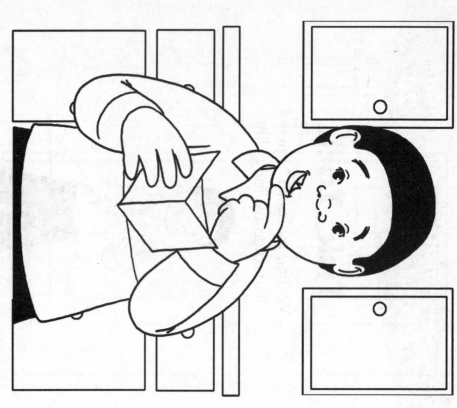

2

That's my room!
I hear the timer go
"tick, tock."
But I can't find it!

7

The room with the broom
had this new clue in place.
It said, "Go to the room
where you sit at noon."

That clue in the bathroom
asked me to find
the room with blue rugs.
Which room has blue rugs?

At the table, this new clue waited.
"Find that place
that keeps food cool."

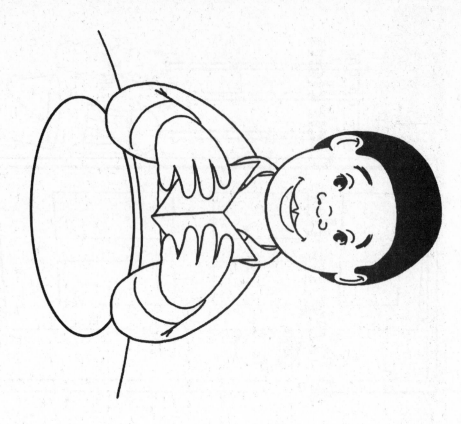

4

That freezer is cold!
That food and juice are frozen.
I took that clue out!
It told me to find that place
where each tooth is brushed!

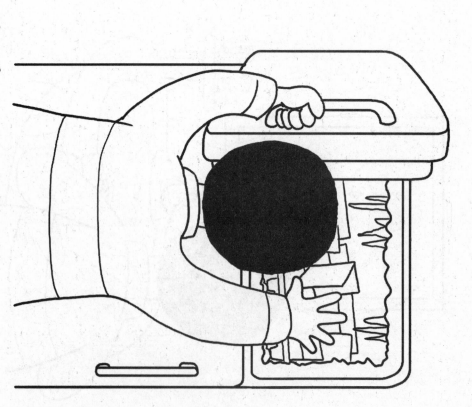

5

A Day in the Garden

Written by Jan Stroud
Illustrated by Tim Ford

Phonics Skill

Suffixes -ly, -ful, -er, -or

brightly	skillful	gardener	peaceful	helpful	hardly
quickly	helper	weekly	teacher	gently	hopeful
fondly	tightly	closely	sweetly	thankful	visitor

Kim smiles sweetly.
She is thankful for this garden.
"Every visitor will like this garden,"
she thought.

8

"The sun shines brightly,"
Kim said to herself.
Kim's mom is a skillful gardener.
Sunny days are spent helping
Mom in her peaceful garden.

2

Kim hugs her mom tightly.
Then she gets back to her work.
"To be a good gardener like Mom,
I will watch closely and work hard,"
Kim said.

7

Kim is helpful.
She can hardly wait.
She quickly runs
to Mom's garden.
Kim is a good helper.

Mom and Kim are hopeful.
This garden is growing well.
"This may be the best garden
we have grown," Mom said,
fondly patting Kim's cheek.

Kim and her mom work
in the garden weekly.
Kim learns from her mom.
"You're a good teacher,"
Kim told her mom.

4

Mom tends big plants.
Kim tends little plants.
When plants look weak,
Kim gently nurses each plant.

5

The Spaceman and Pilot Jack

Written by Santi James
Illustrated by Norby Ramirez

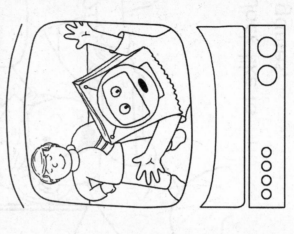

JON

JACK

Next time Jon and Jack play,
Mom and Dad will reuse the tape
to make a funny new film.
Jon and Jack will be stars!

8

Jon and Jack like to
think up games.
Then they play them.
Most of the time
those boys act very silly.

2

Mom and Dad got everything on film!
They rewind the film
and replay it so that
Jon and Jack can see.
Everyone laughs.

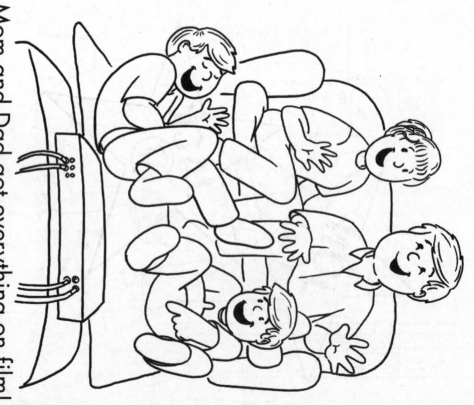

7

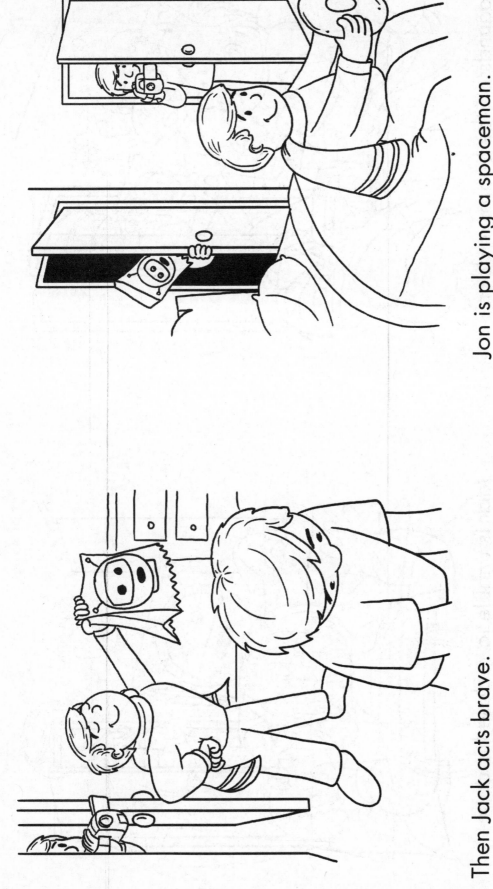

Jon is playing a spaceman.
Jack is playing a space pilot.
Their bedroom is a spaceship.
Jack does a preflight check
of the ship.

Then Jack acts brave.
He unmasks that unhappy spaceman.
Jack tells that spaceman to never
come back.
Jack has saved the day!

Jon pounds on the bedroom door.
Pilot Jack dislikes that noise.
Jack unlocks the door.
He reacts by jumping back
when he sees the spaceman.

4

Jack is unable to reclose his door.
What can he do so
that spaceman can't get him?
He hides behind his bed.

5

Meet Tom Lamb

Written by Karen Vincent

Illustrated by Fred McCabe

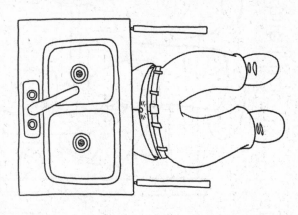

Phonics Skill

Silent Consonants kn, wr, gn, mb

knocked	know	Lamb	wreath	sign
wrapped	wrench(es)	wrist	kneeled	knee
knob	wrong	knocking		

When my wreath was done,
I showed Dad and Tom Lamb.
Tom was finished too.
There was no more knocking
in the water pipes.

8

An old, white truck
pulled into our driveway.
A man knocked
on our door.

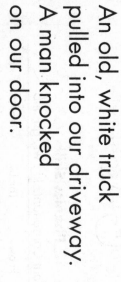

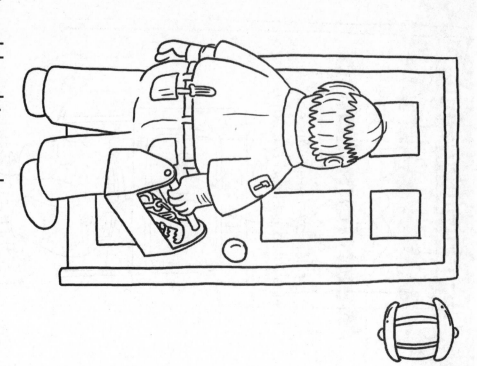

Clink! Clank!
"Oops!" Tom said. "Wrong pipe!"
I held a wrench for Tom
while he looked closer.

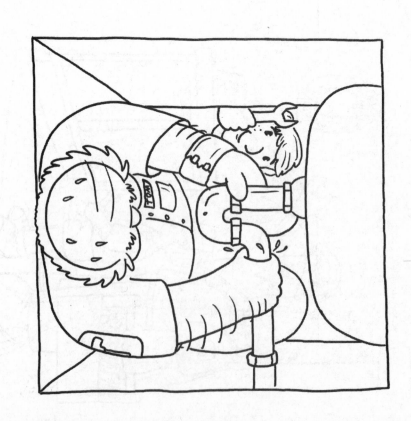

"I know who that is," Dad said.
"It is Tom Lamb.
He has come to fix our pipes."
Dad let the man in.

Tom had many wrenches.
He kneeled down,
put his knee on the ground,
and reached under the sink.
Tom turned a knob.

"What are you making?" Tom asked
as he pulled out his tools.
"It's a flower wreath," I said proudly.
"I made a sign that has my name too."

4

Tom had his arm wrapped.
My dad asked if he had hurt it.
Tom said that he had hit it
with a wrench.
His wrist was still sore.

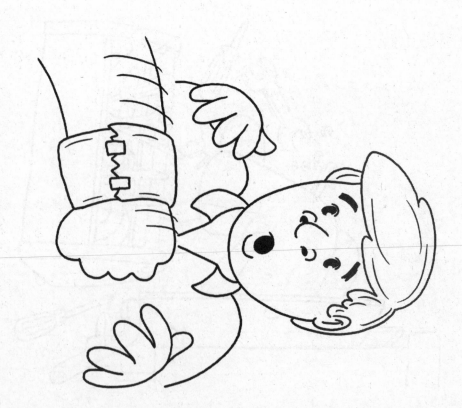

5

Strategic Intervention
Decodable Reader 24

Big Brother Ted

Written by Grace Peterson
Illustrated by Tracey Binder

Phonics Skill
/f/ph, gh

phone   photos   graphs   laugh   phrases

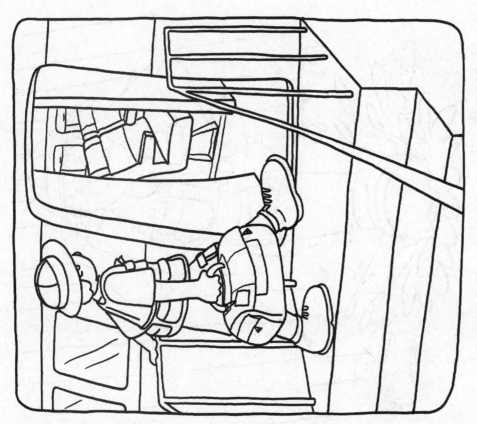

Jim saw more good news in the letter.
Ted is coming home for a visit!
Jim can't wait to be told
Ted's stories in person.

8

Jim has an older brother
who is in another country.
Sometimes Ted calls home
on the phone.
Mostly he writes letters.

2

Last month, it rained so much
that Ted's town flooded.
The roads were under water.
"It was hard to go places," Ted wrote.
"But now the roads are clear."

7

Ted works in hard places.
He helps people who need
clean water, food, or money.

When Ted sends Jim a letter, he
tells stories that make Jim laugh.
He teaches Jim nice phrases
to say in that country.

Jim has many photos
of Ted riding in jeeps,
reading graphs, looking at maps,
and standing beside huge cliffs.

4

Ted sends photos of wild animals
that he sees.
Ted sees bright snakes,
odd birds, and funny bugs.
He has even seen tigers!

5

Strategic Intervention
Decodable Reader 25

A Job for Paul

Written by April Rydell

Illustrated by Jay Fiedermann

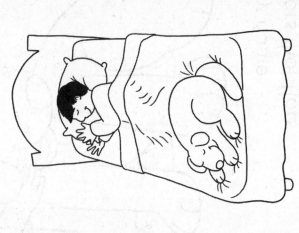

Phonics Skill

Vowels aw, au, au(gh), al

Paul	walk	caught	awful	paw
taught	paws	because	almost	cause
always	naughty	small	tall	

When you think
it's time to get a pet,
just think of Paul and me.
It's no small job having me!

8

Rex is my name.
I have ears that flop
and a tail that wags.
Paul is very good to me.

2

Having me is a hard job.
I am not always so good.
But when I am naughty,
Paul cleans up.

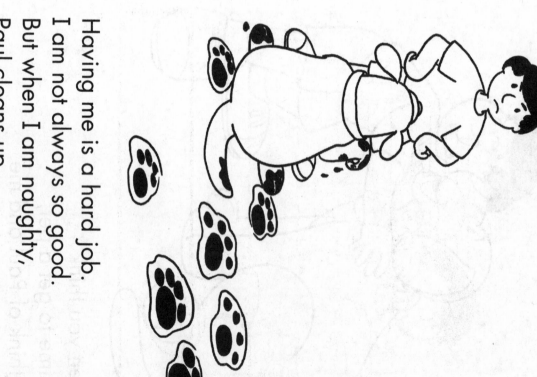

7

Paul must walk me each day.
He holds my leash
so that it will not get caught.
Even when it rains, we walk.

Because I'm his dog,
I walk after Paul.
I try to walk softly,
so my paws don't cause noise.

Paul feeds me twice each day.
When he forgets,
it's not too awful.
I paw gently at his arm
with my dish in my mouth.

4

Paul taught me a trick.
I stand on two paws
and hold two paws up high.
I am almost as tall as Paul!

5

Strategic Intervention
Decodable Reader 26

The Perfect House

Written by Jake Swanson
Illustrated by Sandy Jenkins

Phonics Skill

Contractions 're, 've, 't, 'nt, 'd; Irregular Contractions

we're   I've   they're   doesn't   don't   won't   he'd

That is how those Foxes got their perfect house.

8

Dad Fox is looking
for the perfect house.
This house has to be a good fit
for him, his wife, and Baby Fox.

2

Dad Fox knew this must be
the house he'd dreamed of.
"It is perfect for Baby,
it is perfect for Mom,
and it is perfect for me!" he cried.

7

"We're going to get a house today!"
shouted Dad.
"I've picked some houses to see.
They're just waiting for us!"

Those Foxes went to the third house.
"I like it!" shouted Baby Fox.
"I like it too!" shouted Mom Fox.
"Then I like it too!" shouted Dad Fox.

Those Foxes went to the first house.
"I don't like it," said Baby Fox.
"If Baby doesn't like it,
we won't get it," added Mom.

4

Those Foxes went to the next house.
"I don't like it," said Mom Fox.
"If Mom doesn't like it,
we won't get it," added Dad.

5

Strategic Intervention
Decodable Reader 27

King of the Jungle

Written by Calvin Woods
Illustrated by Carol Nicosia

Phonics Skill

Adding Endings -s, -ed, -ing, -er, -est

loneliest	talking	visits	tried	scampered
sadder	started	crying	skipping	stopped
hopping	cried	trusted	biggest	shouted
thrilled	dancing	singing	nicest	danced
liked	happiest	smiles	purred	replied

Lonny is the happiest king.
Now he smiles and smiles.
"Thanks so much, Bonny!" Lonny purred.
"Anything to help," she replied.

8

Lonny was the loneliest.
He is king of this jungle,
but other beasts don't like
talking with him.
Nobody ever visits.

2

That's what Bonny and Lonny did.
All those animals came.
They danced and sang.
Everyone liked talking with Lonny.
All of them had fun.

7

Lonny tried talking to others,
but most just scampered off.
Lonny got sadder and sadder.
He started crying.

"Let's throw the biggest party!"
shouted Bonny.
She was thrilled to help.
"We can plan dancing and singing.
They will see that you are the nicest."

Bonny Bunny came skipping by.
She saw Lonny crying.
Bonny felt afraid.
Then she stopped to think.
Why did the king cry?

4

Bonny started hopping toward Lonny.
"Hello!" she cried.
Lonny trusted Bonny.
He told Bonny how he felt.

Strategic Intervention
Decodable Reader 28

My First Football Game

Written by Kelley Fulsom
Illustrated by Katy White

Phonics Skill

Common Syllables -tion, -ture

station	section	caution	nation
mentioned	action	motion	captured
picture	future		

We took a picture
with the winning players.
When I see that picture in the future,
it will remind me of the fun we had.

8

My sister is taking me
to my first football game.
I can hardly wait!

2

We saw action in the stands too.
Fans clapped and yelled for each team.
When our team captured the ball
and won, my sister jumped up
and hugged me.

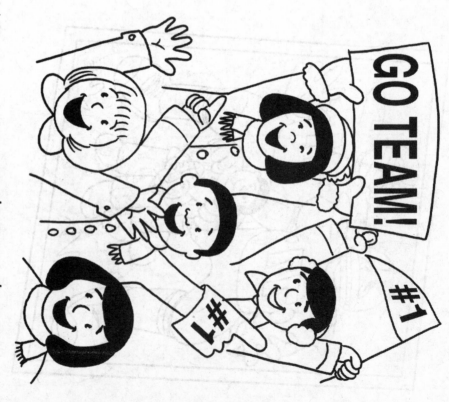

7

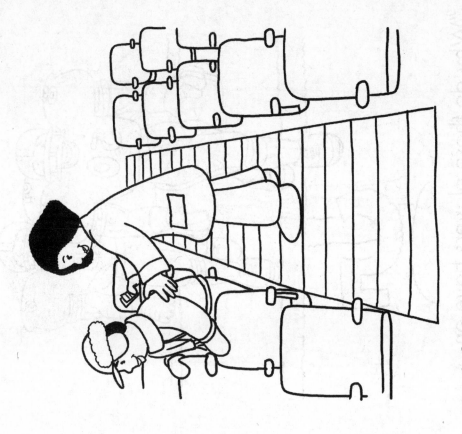

We left the station
and walked to the school.
We found our seats
in the lower section.

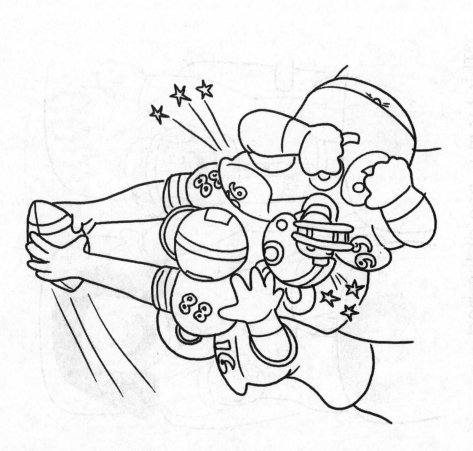
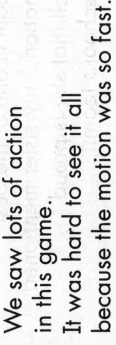

We saw lots of action
in this game.
It was hard to see it all
because the motion was so fast.

"Why do those players have on such big shirts?" I asked. "There are pads under them," my sister replied. "The players must use caution so that they don't get hurt."

4

"This team is one of the best in the nation," my sister mentioned. I can tell that she is proud of her school's team.

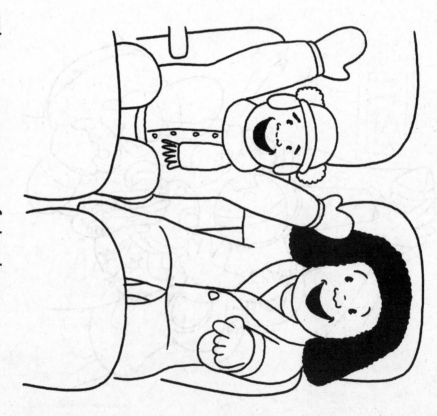

5

In the Darkness

Written by Joel Grand
Illustrated by Vivian Mendez

Phonics Skill

Suffixes -ness, -less.

useless	restless	darkness	brightness
helpless	sleepless	kindness	goodness

As I hugged Mom for her kindness,
I saw that the clock blinked on and off.
"Thank goodness!
Our power is on," Mom cried.
"No more staying in the darkness!"

8

There was an awful storm.
It knocked out our power.
We had no lights.
Many things in our house
were useless.

2

Mom was still in my room
when I woke.
"Why did you stay?" I asked.
"I didn't want you to be afraid,"
she said.

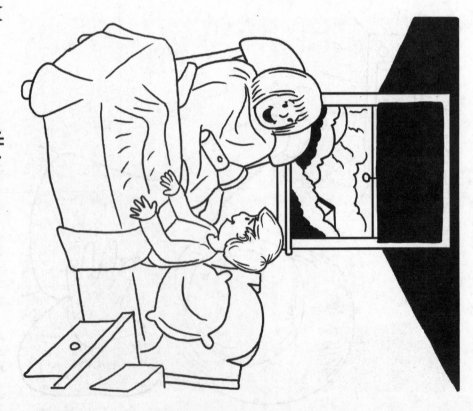

7

We felt restless in the darkness.
We went to look for things to do.
We found something that helped
us in the darkness.

3

When it was bedtime,
Mom and I went to my room.
I was sleepless.
My nightlight did not glow.
Mom stayed with me.

6

Mom found her flashlight.
The light was small,
but its brightness
made us feel brave.
Mom and I went to explore.

"We are not helpless," Mom added.
"We have light, and we have
each other, so we're not lonely."

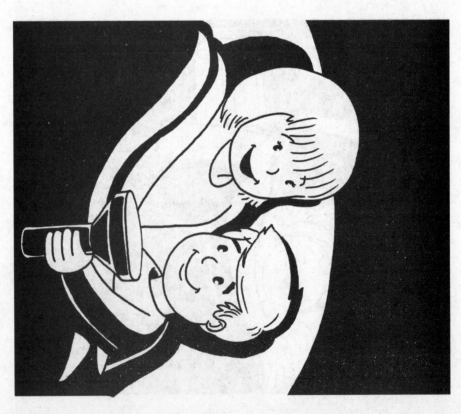

4

5

Strategic Intervention
Decodable Reader 30

The Big Sale

Written by Lisa Vollmer
Illustrated by Alex Conner

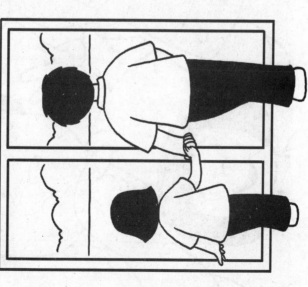

"Mom will want to see these good deals," he noted. "We will bring her here while these prices are low."

8

Jane and her dad went
to Midtown Market to shop
at midday on Sunday.
They found a good sale
at that store.

2

"Maybe we can return midweek,"
Jane said.
"This sale ends at midnight,"
the clerk noted.
Dad looked again at that cheap shirt.

7

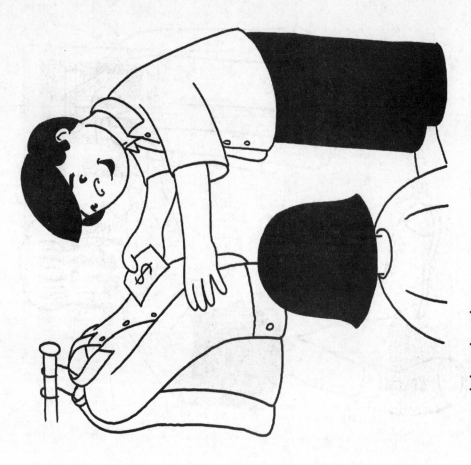

Dad looked at a tag.
"This price can't be right.
I've never seen shirts this cheap!"

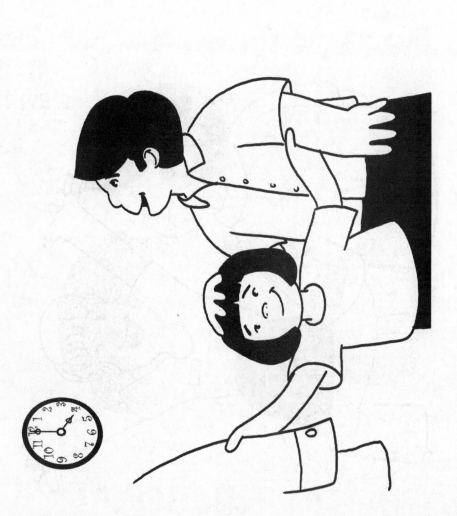
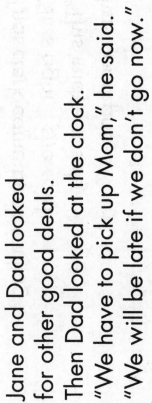

Jane and Dad looked
for other good deals.
Then Dad looked at the clock.
"We have to pick up Mom," he said.
"We will be late if we don't go now."

The clerk came by.
"I will check," she said.
"It might be a misprint,
which would be misleading."
She went to ask her boss.

4

That clerk came back smiling.
"It is right," she said.
"This midyear sale
has good prices."

5